The HERITAGE VILLAGE COLLECTION

1989

A BOOK FOR COLLECTORS

SECOND EDITION

Dedicated to

Ruth Lund
For her inspiration and research in the development
of the Heritage Village Collection.

HERITAGE VILLAGE COLLECTION

1989

including

Dickens' Village
Christmas Carol
NEW ENGLAND VILLAGE
Alpine Village
CHRISTMAS IN THE CITY
and
Little Town of Bethlehem

are protected by United States of America copyright laws.

Reproduction in any form is strictly prohibited.

Worldwide distribution of any or part of the all-inclusive Heritage Village Collection
only through Department 56, Minneapolis, Minnesota, U.S.A.

Library of Congress, National Serials Data Program
ISSN 1043-7037
ISBN 0-9622603-1-2

$\mathcal{L}$ove of holiday traditions sparked the original concept of the Heritage Village Collection. When decorating our homes, we are often drawn to objects reminiscent of an earlier time. Holiday memories wait, hidden in a bit of wrinkled tissue or a dusty box, until that time each year, when rediscovered, we unpack our treasures and are magically transported to a time and place waiting to be remembered.

The first introduction of the Dickens' Village by Department 56 in 1984 was the beginning of the Heritage Village Collection. Extensive research, charming details and the fine handpainting of the seven original porcelain shops and Village Church established them as a "favorite" among collectors.

Other series followed with the introduction of the New England Village, Alpine Village, Christmas in the City, and in 1987, the presentation of the Little Town of Bethlehem. Each of these ongoing collectible series have been researched for authenticity and have the same attention to detail as the original Dickens' Village.

As each of the villages began to grow, limited edition pieces, along with trees, street lamps, and accessory groupings were added to complete the nostalgic charm of these collections. Each piece is stamped in the bottom with its designated series name, title, year of introduction, and Department 56 logo, all assurances of authenticity.

Your Heritage Village Collection will take its place among your other cherished holiday decorations. It will become almost real as each year your imagination brings your village to life.

DEPARTMENT 56 MASTER SCULPTORS: PEI YUAN ZHANG AND PEI TEH ZHANG

$\mathcal{T}$he design and creation of a Heritage Village Collection piece is a time consuming and complicated process. There are many production steps before a piece reaches you, the collector. Each model begins with an original idea. Drawings, sculpting, casting, firing, handpainting and packaging are other steps in this procedure.

This chapter is a step by step outline of how Department 56 creates these collectibles.

An Idea:

In 1984, the artistic team of Ruth and Neilan Lund presented the concept and drawings for the Dickens' Village Collection to Department 56. These drawings of the seven original shops and village church became the cornerstone of the Dickens' series. Working closely together this team researched and developed ideas for the New England Village, Alpine Village, and Little Town of Bethlehem.

Other ideas come from a variety of sources. For example, after many hours of research, Christmas in the City was designed by the Department 56 creative staff.

Collectors also submit ideas for consideration for other pieces that they would like to see produced as additions to their own personal collections.

Drawings:

Similar to a blueprint, scaled drawings must be created for every building. Each side of the piece is drawn in explicit detail, showing windows, shutters, doors, chimneys and architectural features.

Exterior facings such as stonework, woodwork, foundations and roofs are also shown on these drawings. This guide is very important for the next step of the manufacturing process which is sculpting.

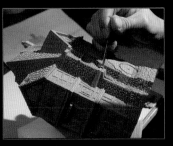

FINISHED ORIGINAL CLAY MODEL

Sculpting:

Pieces take shape beginning with a clay model or prototype. To offset shrinkage during kiln firing, the clay model must be 15% larger than the final product. The wet clay is formed by hand using techniques developed by our sculptors through years of experimentation. Many days are spent on the preparation and formation of the body of each house, followed by the detailing of each individual brick, roof tile, and snow drift.

Attachments such as dormers, pillars, and lamps are sculpted separately with extreme precision to avoid unsightly markings when they will be added on a later stage of production.

Mold Making:

Upon completion of the finely detailed clay sculpture, a mold impression is taken using a specially formulated super-fine plaster. This is called the "mother mold". Through a series of complex processes, requiring a high level of technical skill, the mother mold is used to produce a "case mold". The extra hard, high density composite used to form the case mold is essential to prevent exterior details on the houses from wearing down after extended use of the mold.

Production molds, made of a highly porous plaster mixture, are in turn produced from the case molds. The production molds are separated into as many as six parts which are banded tightly together before the casting process begins.

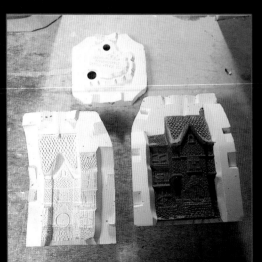

THREE PIECE "MOTHER MOLD"

PIECES READY FOR THE KILN (Background)

Casting:

Slip casting is the first step in the actual production of the Heritage Village houses. Liquid clay, "slip", is poured into the cavity of the production mold. Moisture is drawn out of the clay slip and into the porous plaster mold and a thin wall of clay is formed along the inside of the mold cavity. The excess slip is poured out and the mold is left idle to allow the clay body to harden. Finally, the mold is unbanded and delicately removed.

The result is a hollow, semi-firm clay structure, the beginning of what will eventually become a fine porcelain collectible. Adjustments to the clay body are necessary before the kiln firing process. Mold lines are gently sanded and sponged away, while attachments must be carefully "glued" in their appropriate places using a clay slip mixture. Cutting of windows requires a quick steady hand, after which the piece is set out to dry for up to 24 hours.

Firing:

The kiln firing is the final step in preparation of the porcelain body. Each piece is placed on a circular row of cars which move along a track. At the rate of one every nine minutes, the cars enter the kiln, each carrying up to thirty pieces. After traveling the full length of the 120 foot kiln tunnel, the brittle clay houses are transformed at 1250 degrees Fahrenheit into pure white, rock hard porcelain, through a chemical process known as "reduction".

Handpainting:

The hand painting stage of production is the most labor intensive, requiring the ultimate concentration from our highly skilled artisans. Colors are applied to walls, roofs, and foundations, carefully avoiding details such as windows, shutters, and doors. These features are then painted using smaller brushes. Sometimes antiquing paint is applied to tone or mute brighter colors resulting in the piece having a weathered look.

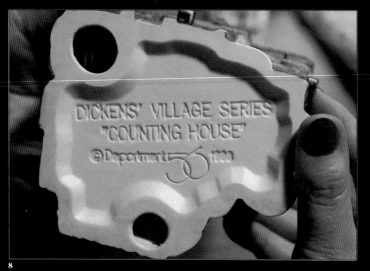

After painting, the houses are put through a special kiln used only for the purpose of adhering the pigments onto the porcelain surface. Kiln temperature is set at 680 degrees Fahrenheit to insure that the paint is color fast and will not rub off during handling and cleaning.

Packaging:

The final step in this long process is packaging. Each model is packed in its own individual styrofoam storage carton and illustrated sleeve. A special compartment in the boxing of all lighted pieces holds the UL approved switched cord and bulb. This method not only protects the pieces during shipping, but provides a convenient way of repacking and storing your collection for many years.

Department 56

Dickens' Village©
COLLECTION

The spirit of Christmas in Victorian England was bustling, hearty, and joyous. Visitors arrived by coach as shoppers scurried about the village gathering gifts and traditional holiday delicacies. This delightful period was captured best by Charles Dickens' in his classic story "A Christmas Carol". The Dickens' Village Collection recreates the festive holiday spirit of this bygone era with an assortment of shops, houses, buildings, and accessories.

The originals of these charming, Dickensian shops were constructed over hundreds of years. Builders used local materials; most buildings were timber-framed, with many parallel, vertical and horizontal beams. Sometimes twigs called "wattle" were interwoven and inserted into the openings formed by these beams. "Daub," a process of applying crude clay and plaster was then layered over the twigs. In other buildings, bricks filled the spaces between the timbers.

he Abel Beesley Butcher Shop was "half-timbered" with the upper story constructed of stone and covered with plaster. Other buildings such as the Church and the Crowntree Inn were completely made of stone. Stonework was often made of rubble, stones of irregular shape and size. Using them gave the walls a roughhewn quality that grows more beautiful with age.

Roofs could be thatched from straw or reeds, like the Green Grocer's shop, or made of clay, stone or slate tiles. Large panes of window glass were costly and hard to ship, so the builders of many shops and cottages bowed to necessity and used small pieces. In doing so, they added a quaint look to these buildings.

There was much to see through these small-paned windows; the rustic Nativity spread near the altar; tiny, hand-made tallow candles to light Christmas trees; plump geese hanging from the butcher's ceiling beams; weary travellers taking their ease before the roaring fire in the inn; heaps of holiday fruit in the Green Grocer's shop; and Christmas cakes, puddings and breads at the Golden Swan Baker.

Through the distinctive curved corner window of the Public House, commonly called the "pub," people could be seen relaxing after a long day's work.

In the connecting Sweet Shop, small window panes were beautifully joined with strips of lead. Curved timbers added still more grace to the building. A favorite treat here was marchpane, which we call marzipan today.

Charles Dickens' novel "The Old Curiosity Shop" has immortalized this charming establishment. The original, an irregularly shaped corner store, has housed a variety of businesses during its long history. Here, it is fittingly joined to a small shop selling rare books.

urning the corner, we find a cobblestone road lined with Merchant Shops. These five shops introduced in 1988 are fine examples of the varied architecture and building styles typical of Dickens' era.

The purveyor of the finest fish and seafood was the Mermaid Fish Shoppe. To tempt shoppers, fresh cockles, mussels, and the catch of the day were displayed in roadside bins.

Passing by the Poulterer, with fresh dressed geese hanging beside its timbered door, we come to Walpole Tailors. This quaint shop-house, constructed of stone and brick, with a heavy stucco exterior, was a family owned business specializing in highland tweed suits and warm woolen greatcoats.

GEO. WEETON WATCHMAKER 1988   MERMAID FISH SHOPPE 1988   POULTERER 1988   WALPOLE TAILORS 1988   WHITE HORSE BAKERY 1988

$\mathcal{D}$ickens was an outspoken champion of the underdog, writing and speaking out on many of the social wrongs that took place during his life. One of his most notable works, "Nicholas Nickleby," is the story of an honorable young man who escapes the drudgery of the boarding school, run for profit by the "not so honorable" Wackford Squeers, and sets out on an adventuresome journey to free himself and his family from the clutches of his miserly uncle, Ralph Nickleby. True to the Dickens' style, virtue triumphs and Nicholas gains the support of trusted friends who help him find his way to freedom.

IVY GLEN CHURCH 1988

WACKFORD SQUEERS

BOARDING SCHOOL

Nicholas Nickleby

*T*magine the laughter of skaters as they glide along on Childe Pond. In this typically Victorian sight, the small brick warming house features shutters that could be latched against the winter wind. Young and old alike would have sat on wooden benches to adjust skates or rest weary ankles.

The variety of windows, cornices, columns and chimneys on the brick Counting House shows the Victorian's love of ornamentation. Inside were equally imposing and heavily decorated offices. The world's best known miser, Ebenezer Scrooge, would have conducted his pinch-penny business from a building like this. The add-on Silas Thimbleton barrister offices revert to timber-and-plaster construction beneath their gay Christmas bunting.

CHILDE POND & SKATERS 1988

COUNTING HOUSE &
SILAS THIMBLETON BARRISTER 1988

15

The twin spires of the red brick Abbey Church rose majestically over the English countryside. Although the massive oak doors under the rose window hung on heavy iron hinges, they opened easily to welcome holiday worshipers. The small, covered door on the side led to the sacristy where sacred vestments were kept. The Holy Cross is a replica of the crosses in the center of the ancient market squares that eventually grew into village greens. Nearby stands a town well, a familiar village landmark.

The Norman Church, with its fortress-like crenelated tower and side portico, is typical of churches built in England after the Norman Conquest in 1066. Until the Norman French forces blended into the English Saxons they had overcome, towers like these served both as belltower and watchtower. Built centuries before Dickens' time, many Norman churches still stand today.

BRICK ABBEY 1987

NORMAN CHURCH 1986 (Limited Edition 3500, Closed 1987).

T. Wells Fruit & Spice boasted of rare and exotic fruit and spices from faraway lands. Because of the rarity and high cost of his goods, only the wealthy could enjoy these luxuries on a daily basis, while commoners looked forward to fruit only on special occasions.

The Booter and Cobbler was the first shop built with a "gambrel" roof. While most roofs during this period had one slope per side, a gambrel roof was unique because it had two slopes per side, with the bottom slope being steeper than the upper slope.

RUTH MARION SCOTCH WOOLENS 1989 (Limited Edition 17,500)

*T*wo Limited Edition pieces were designed and introduced in 1989.

The complexity of the Green Gate Cottage with its green painted fenced courtyard and unusual styling is an exciting edition to the Dickens' Village.

The paned bay windows of the Ruth Marian Scotch Woolens shop are the time consuming feature of this unique design. Over 70 individual window openings, each requiring 4-6 hand-cuts, for a total of over 290 cuts, enable this shop to radiate a warm glow from within.

GREEN GATE COTTAGE 1989 (Limited Edition 22,500)

The brick Chadbury Station typifies the earliest stations that dotted the English countryside. The comfort and speed of rail travel was now beginning to replace travel by coach.

With the advent of rail service, merchants could obtain a wider variety of goods. Freight was claimed in the baggage alcove. Wooden benches provided a place to rest, or passengers could await the train's approach under the protection of the overhang on the platform. Parents warned wide eyed children to stand at a safe distance from the puffing, steam-driven engines and the sparks that flew from their heavy, iron wheels.

Kenilworth Castle proudly bears the coat of arms of the feudal lord who ruled a 16th Century city-within-walls. Thick walls, drawbridges, and battle towers indicate the original purpose of these castles—defense of the domain.

By Victorian times, lords had replaced armaments with agriculture, letting a centralized government provide national defense. They had moved from the drafty castles to elegant, brick and stone manors. Great houses like Chesterton Manor sat on extensive lands, and large staffs of workers were needed to conduct the manor business.

These workers or "cotters" lived nearby in modest dwellings like the Tudor, Thatched and Stone Cottages.

CHESTERTON MANOR 1987 (Limited Edition 7500, Closed 1988)

KENILWORTH CASTLE 1987 (Retired 1988)

TUDOR, THATCHED & STONE COTTAGES 1985 (Retired 1988)

M any village shopkeepers lived above their businesses. The family entrance to the upstairs of the Cottage Toy Shop is on one side of the building and on the other are dovecotes for raising pigeons. Downstairs in the shop rocking horses, toy soldiers, and china dolls set holiday wishes dancing in children's dreams.

Old taverns like Tuttle's Pub had sleeping rooms for travellers and bore plaques boasting of visits from early English kings. The old bread oven used for baking was attached on the outside of the pub. The reason for this was to keep the interior of the Pub cool in the summer.

Much of the social life of the times went on in places like the Thomas Kersey Coffee House. Many famous authors exchanged literary ideas in just such a place. Here, the lower walls are of light brick with darker, ornamental brick trim, and the upper walls are the familiar timber and plaster construction.

COTTAGE TOY SHOP 1986   TUTTLE'S PUB 1986   THOMAS KERSEY COFFEE HOUSE 1986

The heavy wooden ox sled serves a holiday use bringing firewood and a Christmas tree to the farm.

*R*olling fields surround Barley Bree Farm's white buildings. Large field stones form the base of the thick barn walls that provide shelter against winter cold and summer heat for the livestock inside. Both the house and the barn have a thatched roof. Straw and reeds woven into thick mats were laid parallel and overlapped to shed water.

The rubblestone, timber-framed towers of millhouses like Blythe Pond Mill House, seen on page 9, and the Village Mill shown here would have been landmarks dotting the English countryside. The wooden millwheel now stands still in the frozen millpond, but will turn again next spring when the ice goes out and "power" returns to the flowing stream.

The Christmas Carol
COLLECTION

*O*ne of the world's best loved holiday classics is Charles Dickens' "A Christmas Carol." This is the story of Ebenezer Scrooge, a miserly, nasty old money lender, who is visited by three spirits on a cold, lonely Christmas Eve. Scrooge journeys with these spirits through past, present and future, learning from each the true meaning of Christmas. Our interpretation of this classic story results in pieces that enhance and expand the spirit of the Dickens' Village.

The Flat of Ebenezer Scrooge is the latest addition to "A Christmas Carol." From its distinctive door knocker, where Scrooge first sees the ghostly image of Marley's face, to the small room on the top floor, where Scrooge lives, this dwelling is our interpretation of where the story all begins.

CHRISTMAS SPIRITS SET 1989

CHRISTMAS MORNING SET 1989

FEZZIWIG AND FRIENDS SET 1988

*T*he Christmas Spirits accessory set portrays Jacob Marley shackled in chains, Scrooge with the spirit of Christmas past, the bountiful spirit of Christmas present, and the dreadful apparition of Christmas yet to come.

A memory from Scrooge's past is captured in the delightful character set entitled Fezziwig and Friends.

True to the story, this accessory set entitled Christmas Morning, finds Scrooge a changed man. With the true meaning of Christmas in his heart, he tips his hat and joyously proclaims "Merry Christmas" to the Cratchits and Tiny Tim.

Each of the characters in these sets is finely sculpted in porcelain and handpainted in intricate detail.

25

In 1987, Department 56 commissioned Valerie Bunting, an American artist from Utah, to create a three-piece set of limited edition Christmas Carol Dolls. This signed and numbered series of 250 sets portrays Ebenezer Scrooge, Mrs. Cratchit, and Bob Cratchit carrying Tiny Tim. Crafted in the United States, these dolls feature handpainted porcelain heads and hands and are dressed in period costumes.

A companion edition, limited to 350 sets, was introduced in 1988. This three-piece set portrays the Christmas Carol characters on Christmas morning. In his excitement, Scrooge rushes out in his nightclothes to spread his newfound spirit of giving.

Many Americans have taken the nostalgic holiday trip "over the river and through the woods to Grandmother's house," a journey through the countryside. The era of covered bridges, log cabins, and horse drawn sleighs is recreated here in the New England Village Collection.

Weston Train Station is typical of many stations still serving small towns in rural America. The gable window provided extra light in the large waiting room.

The Jacob Adams Farm is an example of an early New England farm. Farmers often built their barns with most door and window openings facing south to avoid blustery north winds. The wooden sides were usually painted red with the foundation made of stones cleared from the field.

A porch on the farmhouse was a necessity. It provided access to cool breezes while working - shelling peas, churning milk into butter, or keeping up with the news while visiting with neighbors.

JACOB ADAMS FARMHOUSE & BARN 1986

Village buildings reflected this neighborly spirit too. The Town Hall with its tiny white cupola was the seat of local government. The white clapboard church is a typical example of the simple Early American form and function style. The General Store carried nearly everything people in the surrounding area needed, from floor to ceiling, stocked shelves and bins lined the walls, while barrels, crates, and sacks formed a narrow pathway through the store.

The Nathaniel Bingham Fabric Store and the Post Office share space in a saltbox structure that is characteristic of New England. The catslide roof gave extra room in the building while maintaining a good angle to shed heavy snow.

Another combined structure is the Livery Stable, where the blacksmith, when necessary, served as a veterinarian or dentist, and the Saddle and Boot Shop where the tanner made harnesses. The Apothecary, which evolved into the modern drugstore, is built from fieldstone the only stone structure in the village.

STEEPLE CHURCH 1986

BRICK TOWN HALL 1986

TOWN HALL

GENERAL STORE

NATHANIEL BINGHAM FABRICS

POST OFFICE

NEW ENGLAND VILLAGE

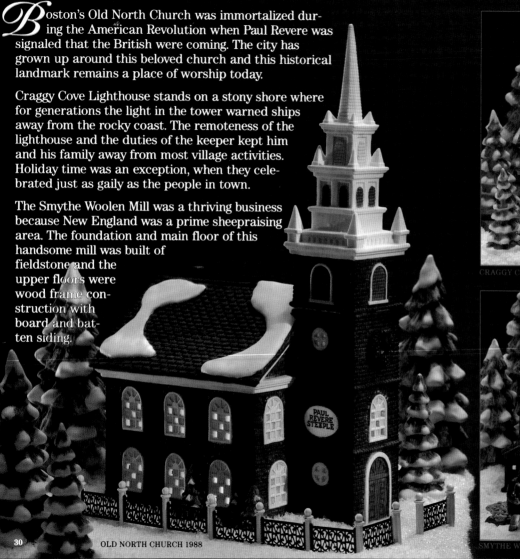

$\mathcal{B}$oston's Old North Church was immortalized during the American Revolution when Paul Revere was signaled that the British were coming. The city has grown up around this beloved church and this historical landmark remains a place of worship today.

Craggy Cove Lighthouse stands on a stony shore where for generations the light in the tower warned ships away from the rocky coast. The remoteness of the lighthouse and the duties of the keeper kept him and his family away from most village activities. Holiday time was an exception, when they celebrated just as gaily as the people in town.

The Smythe Woolen Mill was a thriving business because New England was a prime sheepraising area. The foundation and main floor of this handsome mill was built of fieldstone and the upper floors were wood frame construction with board and batten siding.

CRAGGY COVE LIGHTHOUSE 1987

SMYTHE WOOLEN MILL 1987 (Limited Edition 7500, Closed 1988)

"*D*ashing through the snow" in a one horse open sleigh, we pass the Cherry Lane Shops, other buildings in the New England Village.

The mansard roof of Anne Shaw's Toy Shop was like no other in the village. Shelves were stocked with wonderful handmade toys.

Ben's Barbershop, further down the lane, had a big red and white striped barber pole out front. This square clapboard building had large windows on the first floor and a wooden water reservoir on the roof.

Otis Hayes, the butcher, had his shop next door. This was a small building made of stone where you could purchase smoked meat and hams.

*I*n New England you could stay at one of several rooming houses similar to Ada's Bed and Board. After Ada had raised her family, she was left with a big house and many empty rooms. Being of a hospitable nature, and longing to have people around again, turning her home into a boarding house was a practical matter.

The Alpine Village
COLLECTION

The Alpine Village Collection recreates the charm of a quaint mountain town. Glistening snow and clear lakes fed by icy streams dot this landscape. Windows here have double layers of glass to stave off cold temperatures, and the roofs gently slope to hold heat inside under blanketing layers of snow.

Village life has changed little except that tourist inns and shops have been added. Guests register in the Gastof Eisl to be shown to rooms with beds mounded with billowing feather comforters. During the long winter, flower boxes are filled with greenery and in summer when planted are ablaze with flowers.

The Josef Engel Farm has been in the family for generations. This typical farm has the house and barn joined together. By doing this, heat could be saved and long trips to the barn could be avoided during cold winter months. You can almost hear the ringing of cow bells as the cows graze on the distant hillside.

The Alpine Church with its onion dome is an example of churches sometimes found in villages in Austria and Switzerland. The church tower is the most visible location in town. Often, a large clock is found at the top with its bells ringing on the hour. The melodious chimes become part of the enchantment of this area.

JOSEF ENGEL FARMHOUSE 1987   GRIST MILL 198

CHRISTMAS IN THE CITY©

COLLECTION

usy sidewalks, street corner Santas, friendly traffic cops, and bustling crowds create the mood of the Christmas in the City Collection. During this joyous season, strangers greet each other with a cheery "Merry Christmas". Stores with an array of merchandise in their warmly lit windows beckon shoppers inside.

Within the spired cathedral, the altar is set with the colors of the season. The pipe organ and choir offer the inspiration of Christmas music, and the beautiful stained glass window above the door beckons holiday celebrants in from snowy streets.

Built with common walls, the multi-storied brownstones save costly space and share heat while still providing cozy, self-contained housing for the families inside. High-ceilinged rooms allow plenty of space for tall Christmas trees, and the railings of stairways between floors were decked with holiday greens.

Theatregoers streamed through the elegant foyer and into the Palace Theatre to see "The Nutcracker". The stage door, in back, was the private entrance for the actors. At the conclusion of the performance, some members of the audience would rush around the corner hoping for the chance to catch a glimpse of their favorite stars leaving through this door.

City streets were lined with multi-story buildings with the ground floors occupied by a variety of shops, restaurants, and businesses. Upper floors were home to apartment dwellers. With space at a premium, basements provided room for additional shops and storage.

Signs as individual as the businesses they identify were hung in various places; above doors, on windows, or even painted on the awnings.

TOY SHOP & PET STORE 1987   BAKERY 1987   CHOCOLATE SHOPPE 1988   TOWER CAFE 1987   37

*C*ity Hall was an imposing massive stone structure with many turrets and a large tower on the front with clock faces on all four sides. The roof was made of copper, and with age had turned an elegant shade of federal green.

In front, during the holidays, a dedicated Salvation Army Band could be heard playing cheery Christmas carols.

A bright star in the night sky beckoned travellers to the Little Town of Bethlehem as the miracle of Christmas began. This star guided the Wisemen, who journeyed from distant lands, and the sheperds who left their flocks to join in the joyous celebration. The 12 piece Little Town of Bethlehem Collection authentically reproduces the essence of the birthplace of Jesus. Based on research, this location was a marketplace between Jersualem and Hebron.

Travellers bartered for provisions as they moved through these marketplace towns. They paid for their purchases with gold or jewels, which were a negotiable currency. Potters made vessels of clay that could hold oil, water, wine, and other essentials. At other stands dates, figs, and fresh fruits were available.

The architecture is a faithful rendering of the shape and style of buildings that are thousands of years old. The thick sun-dried brick walls helped keep the interior of these buildings at a comfortable temperature. At night, heat absorbed by the walls during the day warmed the interior and during the day, the coolness absorbed through the night was released.

The flat roofs were built with horizontal beams of tree trunks spanning from wall to wall, with support provided as needed by posts inside. A cross layer of reeds or smaller sticks were placed on these timbers, and the entire structure was covered with earth or clay, beaten down to form a strong mass. Sometimes the top was plastered to make it more waterproof. Access to upper storeys was obtained by ladders set atop flat exterior roofs.

The inn, like other buildings, was also built of sun-dried brick. Typically, the inn grew as demand did; expanding from a single room, additional space for travellers and animals was added as needed.

The essence of this complete village scene will continue to inspire and hearten those who celebrate Christmas.

Little Town of Bethlehem©
COLLECTION

SHOPKEEPERS SET 1987 (Retired 1988)

COVERED WOODEN BRIDGE 1986

MAPLE SUGARING SHED SET 1987

ALPINE VILLAGERS SET 1986

OX SLED 1987

Accessories

FARM PEOPLE & ANIMALS SET 1987

SNOW CHILDREN SET 1988

SILO & HAY SHED 1987

BLACKSMITH SET 1987

CHOCOLATE SHOPPE

Brown Brothers

BOOKS

5¢

Dickens Village

DICKENS VILLAGE SIGN 1987

NEW ENGLAND
VILLAGE

NEW ENGLAND VILLAGE SIGN 1987

Alpine Village

ALPINE VILLAGE SIGN 1987

CHRISTMAS
IN THE
CITY

CHRISTMAS IN THE CITY SIGN 1987

44　CITY PEOPLE SET 1987

SALVATION ARMY BAND SET 1988

CITY BUS & MILK TRUCK SET 1988

City
NEWS STAND

News

CITY NEWSSTAND 1988

FEZZIWIG & FRIENDS SET 1988

CHRISTMAS MORNING SET 1989

Ebenezer Scrooge

EBENEZER SCROOGE

CHRISTMAS SPIRITS SET 1989

CAROLERS SET 1984

VILLAGE WELL & HOLY CROSS 1987

DOVER COACH 1987

CHRISTMAS CAROL FIGURES SET 1986

CHILDE POND & SKATERS SET 1988

47

ELECTRIC TRAIN SET

VILLAGE TRAIN TRESTLE 1988

Nicholas Nickleby

NICHOLAS NICKLEBY CHARACTERS SET 1988

MAPLE CREEK

EIGH 1988

VERED ...TON 1988

VEHICLE SET 1987

CITY WORKERS SET 1987 (Retired 1988)

LIGHTED TREE WITH CHILDREN & LADDER 1986

PORCELAIN TREE SET 1986

STONE BRIDGE 1987

SLEIGHRIDE 1986

NEW ENGLAND WINTER SET 1986

WESTON STATION

VILLAGE EXPRESS

56

VILLAGE EXPRESS ELECTRIC TRAIN SET 1987 (Retired 1988)

51

HERITAGE VILLAGE COLLECTION

Each original Heritage Village Collection™ lighted piece is stamped in the bottom with its designated series name, title, year of introduction*, and Department 56 logo, all assurances of authenticity.

* Year of introduction indicates the year in which the piece was designed, sculpted, and copyrighted. It is possible these pieces may not be available to the collector until the following calendar year.

1987 Continued

1988